Contents

Introduction

The Complete Companions series of psychology textbooks were originally devised to provide everything that students would need to do well in their exams. Having produced *The Complete Companion Student Books*, the *Mini Companions*, and the *Revision and Exam Companions*, the next logical step was to produce a series of *Exam Workbooks* to provide a more hands-on experience for psychology students throughout their course and particularly in the period leading up to the exam.

Each of the *Exam Workbooks* in this series is focused on one particular exam. This book covers the topic of Aggression (Paper 3: Section D). Each two-page spread of psychology in the Student Book has an equivalent set of exam questions and advice in this Exam Workbook. It is designed for you to write in, so that you gain valuable experience of constructing responses to a range of different exam questions.

A distinctive feature of this *Exam Workbook* is the 'scaffolding' that we provide to help you produce effective exam answers. The concept of scaffolding is borrowed from the field of developmental psychology, where it is a metaphor describing the role of more knowledgeable individuals in guiding children's learning and development. Our scaffolding takes the form of providing sentence starters and exam tips for most questions, to help you develop the skill of writing effective exam answers. All of the material used in our scaffolding comes from the Student Book, and you are provided with page references for that book so that you can find the right material to complete the answer.

Guide to your A Level Paper 3 exam (Issues and options in psychology)

This paper contains four sections, each worth 24 marks. Section A is compulsory. For Sections B–D, you choose one topic (e.g. for Section D you choose either Aggression or Forensic Psychology or Addiction) and answer all the questions on that particular topic.

The content of the four sections is as below:

Section A
Issues and debates in psychology

All questions in this section are compulsory. Questions may focus on any of the Issues detailed in the specification (e.g. gender and cultural bias, ethical issues) or Debates (e.g. free will and determinism, the nature-nurture debate, holism and reductionism). There will be a mixture of low (e.g. 1, 2, 3 marks) and high tariff (e.g. 8, 16) marks and also a mixture of AO1 (selection, description), AO2 (application) and AO3 (evaluation) questions. Not all topics will appear in the exam but you need to revise them all as they are all equally likely to appear.

Section B
Relationships; Gender; Cognition and development

You (or more probably your teacher) will have chosen one of these topics to study. Questions can be set on any of the different aspects of these topics that are detailed in the specification (e.g. for 'Relationships', questions might focus on evolutionary explanations for partner preferences, virtual relationships in social media, parasocial relationships etc.). There will be a mix of low and high tariff marks and a mixture of AO1, AO2 and AO3 questions.

Section C
Schizophrenia; Eating behaviour; Stress

In this Section, you have chosen to study schizophrenia. Questions can be set on any of the different aspects of schizophrenia that are detailed in the specification for this topic (e.g. questions might focus on the classification of schizophrenia, biological and psychological explanations, token economies in the treatment of schizophrenia etc.). As with Sections A and B, there will be a mix of low and high tariff marks and a mixture of AO1, AO2 and AO3 questions.

Section D
Aggression; Forensic psychology; Addiction

As with Sections B and C, you will have chosen one of these topics to study. As this workbook is about aggression, then it is likely that this is the topic you are studying. Again, there will be a mix of low and high tariff marks and a mixture of AO1, AO2 and AO3 questions.

The total mark for this paper will be 96 marks and you will have two hours to answer four questions (one from each Section).

for AQA

Psychology
A Level Paper 3

Aggression

The Complete Companion Exam Workbook

Name

OXFORD

OXFORD
UNIVERSITY PRESS

Great Clarendon Street, Oxford, OX2 6DP, United Kingdom
Oxford University Press is a department of the University of Oxford.It furthers the University's objective of excellence in research, scholarship, and education by publishing worldwide. Oxford is a registered trade mark of Oxford University Press in the UK and in certain other countries.

British Library Cataloguing in Publication Data
Data available

978-019-842892-3

1 3 5 7 9 10 8 6 4 2

Paper used in the production of this book is a natural, recyclable product made from wood grown in sustainable forests. The manufacturing process conforms to the environmental regulations of the country of origin.

Printed in Great Britain by Ashford Colour Press Ltd.

Acknowledgements
The publishers would like to thank the following for permissions to use their photographs:

Cover: cynoclub/Shutterstock

Photos: p13: Erik Lam/Shutterstock; **p15:** Eric Isselee/Shutterstock; **p22:** MirasWonderland/Shutterstock; **p24:** Halfpoint/Shutterstock; **p26:** Fabian Faber/Shutterstock; **p33:** steamroller_blues/Shutterstock; **p45:** cynoclub/Shutterstock

Although we have made every effort to trace and contact all copyright holders before publication this has not been possible in all cases. If notified, the publisher will rectify any errors or omissions at the earliest opportunity.

How to use this Exam Workbook

Specification notes
Each spread begins with the AQA specification entry for this particular topic. This tells you what you need to learn and drives the questions that might be asked in your exam.

Student Book page reference
Each spread has a reminder of the pages where you can read about this topic in **The Complete Companion Year 2 Student Book**.

Scaffolding
Most questions include some 'scaffolding' to help you construct an effective response to the question. This takes the form of sentence starters or appropriate links between points. You can then flesh out this material to make a full answer.

Sample answers
In some topics you will find an answer already provided. This gives you some idea of the appropriate level and length of response necessary to gain full marks.

Mark box
Exam questions have different mark 'tariffs'. We have given you an appropriate number of lines in which you can fit your answer. Questions may also be AO1 (description), AO2 (application), or AO3 (evaluation), which will indicate what particular approach you should take in your response.

Questions
Each spread contains sample exam questions. This is not an exhaustive list of all the possible questions you could be asked on this topic, but it gives you the opportunity to practise answering the most common.

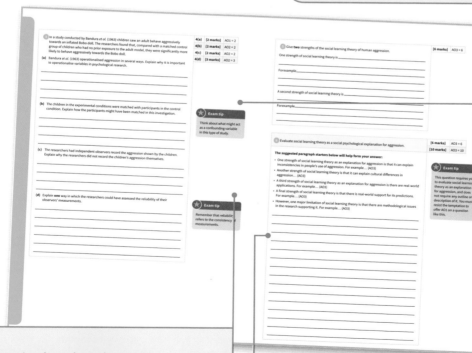

Topic links
Sometimes you will find a link between a topic and the Student Book that we feel will enhance your understanding.

Exam tips
There are helpful exam tips throughout the Exam Workbook. These are general pieces of advice (e.g. the importance of elaborating AO3 points for maximum impact), specific guidance about how to answer a particular question, or how to avoid common mistakes when answering that question.

Essay question
We have included scaffolding for the AO1 and AO3 components of the 16 mark essay questions. We have usually included five AO3 points, although you may choose to use four of these in greater detail.

Types of A Level exam question

Question type	Example	Advice
Simple selection/ recognition	Below are four statements about social learning theory. Which one statement is **not** correct? (1 mark) **A** Children learn about the consequences of aggressive behaviour by watching others being reinforced or punished. **B** In order for social learning to take place, children must form mental representations in their social environment. **C** Children primarily learn their aggressive responses through observation. **D** Only direct experience is responsible for the acquisition of new behaviours.	Questions such as these should be straightforward enough, so the trick is making sure you have selected the right answer to gain maximum marks. If you aren't sure which answer is the right one, try crossing through those that are obviously wrong, thus narrowing down your options. Note also that sometimes (as here), the question requires you to identify which statement is incorrect, so careful reading is vital.
Description questions (e.g. Describe, Outline, Identify, and Name)	Outline the disinhibition explanation of media influences in aggression. (4 marks) Briefly outline what is meant by the term 'fixed action pattern'. (2 marks)	To judge how much to write in response to a question, simply look at the number of marks available and allow about 25 words per mark. If the sole command word is 'Name' or 'Identify', there is no need to develop a 25 word per mark response, simply identifying or naming (as required by the question) is enough.
Differences/Distinguish between	Distinguish between dispositional and situational explanations of aggression in prisons. (4 marks)	You might be tempted to ignore the instruction to 'distinguish between' and simply outline the two terms or concepts named in the question. This is not what is required, and would not gain credit. Words such as 'whereas' and 'however' are good linking words to illustrate a difference between two things.
Applying knowledge	A prison warden was concerned about prisoners using mobile phones. She asked an electronics expert to block all mobile phone signals inside the prison. The system was successful, and calls could neither be made nor received by the prisoners. Within a month, assaults on prison officers increased dramatically. Use your knowledge of explanations of institutional aggression to explain why the number of assaults on prison officers might have increased dramatically. (4 marks)	In these AO2 questions, you will be provided with a scenario (the question 'stem') and asked to use your psychological knowledge to provide an informed answer. You must make sure that your answer contains not only appropriate psychological content, but that this is set explicitly within the context outlined in the question stem.
Research methods questions	You will be given a description of a study and then a number of short questions such as: (a) Write a suitable directional hypothesis for this study. (3 marks) (b) Give two reasons why this study is an example of a 'field experiment'. (2 marks)	Most research methods questions are set within the context of a hypothetical research study. This means that your answers must also be set within the context of that study. If you don't set your answers within the specific context of the study, you cannot receive full marks.
Maths questions	(a) Calculate the mean percentage of time that is actually spent watching TV per week. Show your calculations. (2 marks) (b) Calculate the modal number of hours children spend watching TV per week. Explain your answer. (2 marks)	'Maths' questions can appear anywhere on the paper, and can assess your ability to carry out simple calculations, construct graphs, and interpret data, e.g. in this question, a correct answer and appropriate working are necessary for maximum marks.
Evaluation questions	Evaluate situational explanations of institutional aggression. (4 marks)	It is important that you elaborate your evaluative points for maximum marks. We have shown you how to achieve this through the 'scaffolding' feature.
Mixed description and evaluation questions	Briefly outline the evolutionary explanation of aggression and give **one** limitation of this explanation. (6 marks)	Not all questions are straightforward 'description only' or 'evaluation only', but may be mixed. As a rule of thumb, in questions like these you should divide your AO1 and AO3 content equally.
Extended writing questions	Outline and evaluate the role of the MAOA gene in aggression. (8 marks) Discuss research into media influences on aggression. (16 marks)	As a rough guide, 200 words would be appropriate for an answer to an 8-mark question. For a 16 mark question between 400–500 words would be appropriate.
Extended writing questions with specific instructions	Thomas has a phobia of clowns. He relates this to a scary experience he had as a child. He was at the circus when a clown jumped up from the row behind Thomas and startled him so much that his parents had to leave before the show ended. Thomas was so disturbed that he has not even been able to look at a picture of a clown since, let alone go anywhere near one. Describe and evaluate the two-process model as an explanation of phobias. Refer to the example of Thomas as part of your answer. (16 marks)	Some extended writing questions not only require a discussion of a particular theory, model, etc. (i.e. AO1 and AO3), but also have an additional requirement. This example requires you to discuss not only the two-process model of phobias but to do this in the context of the stimulus material provided. Although the model is the key requirement of the question, don't make the mistake of assuming that the applied aspect of the question is less important.

The way your answers are marked

Questions and mark schemes

Examiners mark your answers using mark schemes and marking criteria. These vary from question to question, depending on the specific demands, but below are some examples.

1-mark questions: 1 mark is given for an accurate selection of the right answer or an appropriate identification. Giving the wrong answer or selecting more than one alternative from those available would result in 0 marks.

2-mark questions: For questions such as '*Identify the level of measurement used in this study. Explain your answer*', 1 mark would be given for identifying the correct level of measurement, and 1 mark for explaining why this is the case. Other 2-mark questions such as 'Calculate the mean score from this data, and show your calculations' have two requirements (i.e. the correct answer and appropriate workings), which would receive 1 mark each.

3-mark questions: These questions might focus on a descriptive point, e.g. '*Outline one explanation of…*', where the mark awarded would reflect the detail, accuracy, and overall organisation of your answer. They can also be evaluative, e.g. '*Give one limitation of the statistical infrequency definition of abnormality*'. The number of marks awarded in these AO3 questions is largely determined by the degree of elaboration of your critical point.

4-mark questions: Descriptive and evaluative questions can sometimes be assigned 4 marks, so will require slightly more detail or elaboration than you would write for a 3-mark question. It is useful to try to write the same number of 'points' as the marks available. You may be familiar with the PEEL (Point, Evidence, Explanation, Link) approach that involves making four different statements for a 4-mark AO3 question. Sometimes 4-mark questions are simply two 2-mark questions in disguise, i.e. they contain two specific components, each worth 2 marks.

6-mark questions: These can have very different requirements (e.g. description only, description plus application, or evaluation only), in which case their actual wording varies, e.g. you may come across a question such as '*Describe research into forgetting*' (6 marks) or '*Evaluate Bowlby's maternal deprivation theory*' (6 marks). For each of these you need to decide what is an appropriate level of breadth (how many studies for the first question, how many critical points for the second) and depth (how much detail, how much elaboration). Usually the answer is two, (i.e. describe two studies) as this is a suitable compromise in the need for both breadth and depth in these questions.

8 and 16-mark questions: Questions above 6 marks are generally referred to as 'extended writing' questions. They always have more than one requirement, so examiners will be assessing (usually) both AO1 and AO3 in what is effectively a short essay response. There are four main criteria that an examiner will be looking for in extended writing answers.

Description (AO1) – have you described the material accurately and added appropriate detail? There are a number of ways in which you can add detail. These include expanding your description by going a bit deeper (i.e. giving more information rather than offering a superficial overview), providing an appropriate example to illustrate the point being made, or adding a study (which adds authority and evidence of wider reading).

Evaluation (AO3) – have you used your critical points effectively? Have you elaborated the points you have made? Examiners will be assessing whether you have made the most of a critical point. A simple way is to identify the point (e.g. that there is research support), justify the point (e.g. provide the findings that back up your claim) and elaborate the point (e.g. link back to the thing being evaluated, demonstrate how research support strengthens a theory or adds support to a research study). In this Exam Workbook we have aimed at writing 30 words of evaluation per mark available for AO3.

- 8-mark question = 4 marks for AO3 and so 120 words of evaluation

- 16-mark question = we have worked on the assumption that you would use five AO3 points of 60 words each. However, you might decide to just use four of the AO3 points we provide and expand each to 75 words. This is entirely appropriate.

Organisation – does your answer flow and are your arguments clear and presented in a logical manner? This is where planning pays off as you can organise a structure to your answer before you start writing. This is always more effective than just sticking stuff down as it occurs to you!

Specialist terminology – have you used the right psychological terms (giving evidence that you have actually understood what you have read or been taught) rather than presented your material in lay (i.e. non-specialist) language? This does not mean you have to write in an overly formal manner. Students often mistakenly believe that they have to use the sorts of words that they would never use in everyday life!

How do examiners work out the right mark for an answer?

Mark schemes are broken down into different levels. Each of these levels has a descriptor, which describes what an answer for that level should look like i.e. an average performance for that range of marks. Examiners will first choose the level they think the answer is and then use the 'magnet effect'. This means once they have decided the level, they will decide whether it is closer to the level above (pulling it to the top of that level), closer to the one below (pulling marks to the bottom of the level) or just in the middle.

Answers

All answers for this Exam Workbook can be found at:

www.oxfordsecondary.co.uk/completecompanionsanswers

Specification notes

Neural and hormonal influences in aggression, including the role of the limbic system, serotonin, and testosterone.

Year 2 Student Book
Pages 228–229

---

1 Below are four statements about neuronal and hormonal influences in aggression. Which **one** statement is correct?

Tick **one** box only.

[1 mark] AO1 = 1

A	Increased serotonin levels are associated with increased aggression levels in humans.	
B	Increased norepinephrine levels are associated with increased aggression levels in humans.	
C	Stimulation of certain areas of the amygdala is associated with increased aggression in non-humans.	
D	Serotonin levels affect the hippocampus and lead to increased aggression.	

Topic link

You can find out more about the biological approach on pages 114–115 of the Year 1 Student Book.

---

2 Outline the role of neural mechanisms in aggression.

[3 marks] AO1 = 3

SAMPLE ANSWER: *The amygdala, which is in the limbic system, coordinates behaviour that helps to satisfy basic urges, such as aggression. It evaluates sensory information and prompts a response. If certain areas are stimulated, animals respond aggressively.*

Exam tip

In questions 2 and 3, you are only required to show your AO1 skills. Never offer any evaluation unless you are asked to.

---

3 Outline the role of hormonal mechanisms in aggression.

[4 marks] AO1 = 4

Testosterone acts on _____

_____

_____

_____

If testosterone levels are high, then _____

_____

_____

_____

4 A research team was interested in the relationship between the volume of the amygdalae and trait aggression. They studied 20 healthy men with no history of mental disorders. Assessments of amygdalae volume were made using an MRI scanner. The measurements were taken by two research assistants, and judged to be reliable. Trait aggression was measured using the Life History of Aggression Assessment (LHAA), which has high concurrent validity. The research team found a correlation of −0.65 between amygdalae volume and trait aggression.

4(a)	[3 marks]	AO2 = 3
4(b)	[3 marks]	AO1 = 3
4(c)	[2 marks]	AO2 = 2
4(d)	[1 mark]	AO1 = 1

(a) Outline **one** way in which the reliability of the research assistants' measurements could have been assessed.

_____

_____

_____

_____

_____

_____

 Exam tip

Remember that reliability refers to the consistency of a measurement, whereas validity is concerned with whether something measures what it says it measures.

(b) The LHAA has 'high concurrent validity'. Explain what is meant by the term concurrent validity, and outline one way in which it can be assessed.

_____

_____

_____

_____

_____

_____

(c) The researchers analysed their data using Pearson's test. Give **two** reasons why this test was an appropriate test to use.

_____

_____

_____

_____

(d) Name an alternative test that could have been used instead of Pearson's test.

_____

_____

5   Outline and evaluate neural **and/or** hormonal mechanisms in aggression.

[16 marks]   AO1 = 6   AO3 = 10

The suggested paragraph starters below will help form your answer:

- The limbic system is an area of the brain that... (AO1)
- The amygdalae are responsible for... (AO1)
- If serotonin levels are low... (AO1)
- Testosterone's role in aggression is... (AO1)
- Research studies support the view that the amygdala plays a role in aggression. For example, Pardini *et al.* ... (AO3)
- Serotonin's role in aggression is supported by research with non-human animals. For example... (AO3)
- Serotonin's role in aggression is also supported by research with humans. For example, Duke *et al.* ... (AO3)
- The claim that testosterone is involved in aggression is supported by Dabbs *et al.'s* research. They found... (AO3)
- However, the role of testosterone has been challenged by studies failing to find an association between it and human aggression. For example... (AO3)

 Exam tip

For your AO1, you can choose to explain neural or hormonal mechanisms in detail, or both mechanisms in less detail.

Specification notes

Genetic factors in aggression, including the MAOA gene.

Year 2 Student Book
Pages 230–231

[1 mark] AO1 = 1

1 Which **one** of the following claims about the MAOA gene and aggression is true?

Tick **one** box only.

A	There is no relationship between the MAOA gene and aggression in both humans and non-humans.	
B	The relationship between the MAOA gene and aggression has only been found in non-humans.	
C	People with the low-activity version of the MAOA gene who were maltreated as children are less likely to respond aggressively when provoked.	
D	People with the low-activity version of the MAOA gene who were maltreated as children are more likely to respond aggressively when provoked.	

 Topic link

You can find out more about the role of genetic factors in the biological approach on pages 114–115 of the Year 1 Student Book.

[4 marks] AO1 = 4

2 Outline the role of genetic factors in aggression.

Twin studies have found that _____

_____

Adoption studies have found that _____

_____

Research suggests that the MAOA gene is associated with aggression. The role of this gene is

_____

A variant of this gene _____

_____

[4 marks] AO2 = 4

3 A study of almost 900 violent offenders in Finland claims that there are two genes associated with violent crime. Evidently, those offenders with the genes were thirteen times more likely to have a history of repeated violent behaviour.

Use your knowledge of research into genetic factors in aggression to briefly evaluate the findings reported above.

The connection between genetic factors and aggression is far from straightforward because

_____

_____

It could be argued that environmental factors _____

_____

_____

Therefore, it is difficult to _____

_____

 Exam tip

The question asks about 'the findings reported above', so remember to contextualise your answer.

4　A teacher worked in a school where she taught eight pairs of identical twins. She decided to conduct a small-scale study in which she rated each twin on a seven-point scale according to how physically aggressive towards other children she judged them to be. She believed that if one member of a twin pair was rated as being aggressive, the other one would be as well.

4(a)	[3 marks]	AO2 = 3
4(b)	[2 marks]	AO2 = 2
4(c)	[2 marks]	AO2 = 2
4(d)	[2 marks]	AO2 = 2

(a) Write a suitable hypothesis for this investigation.

_____

_____

_____

_____

_____

_____

 Exam tip

A hypothesis is a precise and testable statement about the assumed association between variables.

(b) Explain why the teacher's study might have been improved by using independent observers to rate the twins' aggression.

_____

_____

_____

_____

 Exam tip

The word 'address' means you need to write about how the teacher would deal with the ethical issue.

(c) Identify **one** ethical issue raised by the teacher's study, and suggest how she might address it.

_____

_____

_____

_____

(d) The teacher used a Spearman's rho test to analyse her data. Give **two** reasons why she chose this test.

_____

_____

_____

_____

5 Briefly evaluate the claim that the MAOA gene plays a role in aggression.

[4 marks]   AO3 = 4

SAMPLE ANSWER: The claim that the MAOA gene plays a role in aggression is supported by research findings. For example, Tiihonen et al. found that extremely violent behaviour in Finnish prisoners was associated with the MAOA-L gene. There was no substantial evidence for this gene in non-violent offenders. This suggests that the MAOA gene does play a role in some types of aggression.

[16 marks]   AO1 = 6   AO3 = 10

6 Outline and evaluate research into the role played by genetic factors in aggression.

The suggested paragraph starters below will help form your answer:

- Twin studies are one way in which genetic factors in aggression have been studied. For example… (AO1)
- Adoption studies are a second way in which the role played by genetic factors in aggression has been studied. For example… (AO1)
- A third way in which the role played by genetic factors has been studied is by using meta-analysis. For example… (AO1)
- One strength of research into the role played by genetic factors in aggression is that it has been successful in identifying a gene associated with aggressive behaviour. For example… (AO1)
- However, one limitation of this research concerns the samples studied. For example… (AO3)
- A second limitation concerns the assessment of aggression in this research. For example… (AO3)
- A third limitation is that it is difficult to determine the role played by genetic factors from this research. For example… (AO3)
- A final limitation is that the influence of a gene associated with aggression has been challenged. For example… (AO3)

Exam tip

This question requires you to show both your AO1 skills ('outline') and your AO3 skills ('evaluate'). 6 marks are allocated to AO1. There are also 6 marks for AO3 if the question is worth 12 marks, and 10 if the question is worth 16 marks. This means choosing three of these AO3 points for 12 marks and four or five of them for 16 marks.

Specification notes

The ethological explanation of aggression, including reference to innate releasing mechanisms and fixed action patterns.

Year 2 Student Book
Pages 232–233

[1 mark] AO1 = 1

1　Below are four statements about fixed action patterns. Which **one** statement is **false**?

Tick **one** box only.

A	Each fixed action pattern has a specific trigger or sign stimulus.	
B	Fixed action patterns can be changed or stopped after they have been triggered.	
C	Fixed action patterns are produced by a neural mechanism called an innate releasing mechanism.	
D	Fixed action patterns are innate, with no learning involved.	

[4 marks] AO1 = 4

2　Outline the ethological explanation of aggression.

Aggression happens when a sign stimulus triggers _____

_____

This then releases a fixed action pattern, which is _____

_____

_____

Action specific energy is the energy needed for _____

_____

_____

> ★ **Exam tip**
>
> Writing about ritualistic aggression would also receive credit on this question.

[4 marks] AO3 = 4

3　Give **two** limitations of the ethological explanation of aggression.

One limitation of the ethological explanation of aggression is _____

_____

_____

_____

A second limitation of this explanation is _____

_____

_____

_____

4 People who are keen aquarium hobbyists know that only one male Siamese fighting fish can occupy an aquarium at a time. The sight of another male acts as a 'sign stimulus', which activates a neural network that communicates with motor control circuits and causes certain behaviours to occur. The male Siamese fighting fish responds to the presence of another male by spreading his fins, shuddering his body, and generally appearing much larger than his resting size.

Using the example above, explain what is meant by the term 'fixed action pattern'.

A fixed action pattern is _____

_____

_____

For example, the Siamese fighting fish _____

_____

_____

[3 marks] | AO1 = 2 | AO2 = 1

> ⭐ **Exam tip**
>
> The question asks about 'the example above', so you must contextualise your answer.

---

5 In the presence of another male, the three-spined stickleback's most common aggressive behaviour is biting. An ethologist wanted to know if the frequency of biting differed in the presence of a 'dummy conspecific', that is, a model resembling a stickleback suspended from the middle of a thin metal rod. The researcher tested 16 randomly sampled sticklebacks from a local pet shop. He found that 10 bit the live stickleback more, 3 bit the model more, and 3 bit both the same number of times.

5(a) | **[1 mark]** | AO2 = 1
5(b) | **[2 marks]** | AO1 = 2
5(c) | **[2 marks]** | AO2 = 2
5(d) | **[4 marks]** | AO2 = 4

(a) What was the researcher's aim in this study?

_____

_____

(b) The researcher used a random sample of sticklebacks. Explain what is meant by a random sample.

_____

_____

_____

_____

(c) The researcher analysed his results using a sign test. Give **two** reasons why it was appropriate to use a sign test in this study.

_____

_____

_____

_____

> ⭐ **Exam tip**
>
> Was the researcher looking for a difference or a correlation? What type of experimental design was used?

(d) The researcher calculated a sign test value of $s = 3$. Using the information in the item above and the table below, what conclusion can the researcher draw about the sticklebacks' behaviour? Explain your answer.

_____

_____

_____

_____

_____

_____

_____

_____

_____

	0.05 (one-tailed)	0.025 (one-tailed)
	0.10 (two-tailed)	0.05 (two-tailed)
N = 12	2	2
N = 13	3	2
N = 14	3	2
N = 15	3	3
N = 15	4	3

The calculated value must be EQUAL TO or LESS THAN the tabled value for significance at the level shown.

Exam tip

The 'calculated value' is the value obtained when the test is used. The 'tabled' (or 'critical') value is the value it is compared with in order to make a decision about statistical significance.

---

6 Discuss the ethological explanation of aggression.

[16 marks] | AO1 = 6 | AO3 = 10

The suggested paragraph starters below will help form your answer:

- Aggression happens when a sign stimulus triggers… (AO1)
- This then releases a… (AO1)
- Lorenz's hydraulic model… (AO1)
- Some aggressive behaviour may be ritualised in the form of threat displays… (AO1)
- One limitation of the ethological explanation of aggression is that fixed action patterns are not simply innate… (AO3)
- Another limitation of the ethological explanation is that a human fixed action pattern for aggression is no longer adaptive… (AO3)
- One weakness of Lorenz's hydraulic model is that… (AO3)
- A final limitation of the ethological explanation is that Lorenz's idea of 'instinctive inhibitions' is not supported by evidence… (AO3)
- However, one strength of ethological explanations is that ritualised aggression is seen in humans, and has the same benefits as for non-humans. For example… (AO3)

_____

_____

_____

_____

_____

Exam tip

Remember to signal to the examiner when you are evaluating, by using phrases like, 'One research study that supports…' or 'One limitation of research…'

Specification notes
Evolutionary explanations of human aggression.

Year 2 Student Book
Pages 234–235

---

1 Which **one** of the following statements about evolutionary explanations of aggression is **false**?

Tick **one** box only.

[1 mark] AO1 = 1

A	Evolutionary explanations of aggression are concerned with its adaptive functions.	
B	Aggression is a maladaptive behaviour because its benefits are always outweighed by its costs.	
C	Aggression is believed to have evolved because it solved challenges faced by our ancestors.	
D	Aggression would become more widespread in the gene pool if it solved challenges faced by our ancestors.	

---

2 Outline **one or more** evolutionary explanations of human aggression.

[4 marks] AO1 = 4

Evolutionary explanations claim that we are aggressive because _____

_____

For example, men might be aggressive towards women because _____

_____

_____

Men might be aggressive towards other men because _____

_____

_____

> ★ **Exam tip**
>
> Remember that evolutionary explanations are based on the premise that the human brain comprises a number of adaptations to cope with the various challenges associated with group living.

---

3 A researcher conducted a self-report study of cultural differences in men and women's reactions to sexual infidelity. She found that when participants from seven nations were asked how jealous they would feel over a partner having 'satisfying sexual relations with someone else', men did not have higher ratings than women in any of the nations studied.

3(a) [4 marks] AO3 = 4

(a) The psychologist could have obtained her self-report data either by interviewing the participants or by using questionnaires. Explain **one** strength **and one** limitation of using **either** interviews **or** questionnaires in psychological research.

_____

_____

_____

_____

_____

_____

_____

_____

(b) Identify an appropriate sampling method for this study and justify your choice.

3(b)	[2 marks]	AO2 = 2
3(c)	[1 mark]	AO2 = 1
3(d)	[1 mark]	AO2 = 1

_____

_____

_____

_____

(c) Identify the level of measurement used in the study described above.

_____

_____

(d) The researcher predicted that men and women would differ in their ratings of jealousy. Suggest an appropriate statistical test that could have been used to analyse the data.

_____

_____

---

4 Archaeologists have found prehistoric skeletal remains showing evidence of skull and rib fractures. These can only be explained in terms of the victim being assaulted with a club or a weapon that stabs. Humans, it seems, have a long history of being violent towards each other.

[4 marks] AO1 = 4

Outline **one** explanation of why the behaviours described above could have evolved.

Evolution says that we are aggressive because _____

_____

It says men may be aggressive towards other men because _____

_____

_____

So the reason skeletal remains have skull and rib fractures is _____

_____

_____

---

5 Give **two** limitations of the evolutionary explanation of human aggression.

[6 marks] AO1 = 3 AO3 = 3

One limitation of evolutionary explanations of human aggression is _____

_____

_____

A second limitation of evolutionary explanations of human aggression is _____

_____

_____

> ⭐ **Exam tip**
>
> Remember that you have been asked about limitations (weaknesses), rather than strengths.

6 Evaluate evolutionary explanations of human aggression.

| [6 marks] | AO3 = 6 |
| [10 marks] | AO3 = 10 |

The suggested paragraph starters below will help form your answer:

- One strength of evolutionary explanations for human aggression is that research supports the idea that aggression is linked to status. For example… (AO3)
- One weakness of evolutionary explanations is that they fail to explain the levels of cruelty found in human conflict… (AO3)
- A second weakness of the evolutionary explanation is that sex differences in aggression may be due to socialisation, not evolution… (AO3)
- A third weakness is that evolutionary explanations for aggression in warfare are gender biased. For example… (AO3)
- One potential weakness of evolutionary explanations of aggression is that aggressive behaviour is also maladaptive. For example… (AO3)

Exam tip

This question requires you to evaluate evolutionary explanations, and does not require any outline or description of these explanations. You must resist the temptation to offer AO1 on a question like this.

Specification notes

Social psychological explanations of human aggression, including the frustration–aggression hypothesis.

Year 2 Student Book
Pages 236–237

---

1 Which **one** of the following is a claim made by the frustration–aggression hypothesis of aggression?

[1 mark]   AO1 = 1

Tick **one** box only.

A	Frustration never leads to some form of aggression.	
B	Frustration always leads to physical aggression.	
C	Frustration always leads to some form of aggression.	
D	Frustration and aggression are inbuilt characteristics.	

 Exam tip

Even though multiple choice questions look easy, it is important to read each option carefully before giving your answer.

---

2 Outline the frustration–aggression hypothesis.

[4 marks]   AO1 = 4

The frustration–aggression hypothesis says that aggression is the result of _____

_____

This leads to the arousal of an aggressive drive , which _____

_____

After being aggressive, we experience catharsis. This is _____

_____

Sometimes it isn't possible to behave aggressively towards the source of our frustration, so instead we _____

_____

 Exam tip

There is no requirement to offer evaluation on this question, so do not be tempted to do so.

---

3 A researcher asked a class of 30 primary school children to fill in a simple form about themselves. They were promised an extra five minutes in the playground if they could complete the form in two minutes. Although the children did not know it, half of them had been given pens that did not work properly, making it impossible for them to complete the form. As the researcher was leaving, she told the class teacher which children could have the extra five minutes in the playground. When the researcher had left, the teacher asked each child individually if they thought the researcher was 'nasty' or 'nice'. The results are shown in the table below:

	Number calling the researcher 'nice'	Number calling the researcher 'nasty'
Pen worked correctly	12	3
Pen did not work correctly	4	11

(a) Write a directional hypothesis for this study.

_____

_____

_____

_____

_____

_____

_____

3(a)	[3 marks]	AO2 = 3
3(b)	[2 marks]	AO2 = 2
3(c)	[1 mark]	AO2 = 1
3(d)	[2 marks]	AO3 = 2

(b) Give **two** reasons why this study is an example of a 'field experiment'.

_____

_____

_____

_____

Topic link

You can find out more about different types of experiment on pages 186–189 of the Year 1 Student Book.

(c) Identify the level of measurement used in this study.

_____

_____

(d) The researcher used a chi-squared test to analyse the data. She calculated the number of degrees of freedom as 1, and her chi-squared value was 6.56. Using the table below, explain whether or not this value is significant at the 0.05 level for a one-tailed test.

_____

_____

_____

_____

_____

Exam tip

The 'calculated value' is the value obtained when the test is used. The 'tabled' (or 'critical') value is the value it is compared with in order to make a decision about statistical significance.

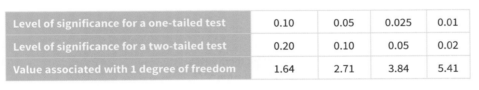

Level of significance for a one-tailed test	0.10	0.05	0.025	0.01
Level of significance for a two-tailed test	0.20	0.10	0.05	0.02
Value associated with 1 degree of freedom	1.64	2.71	3.84	5.41

To be significant at the level shown, the calculated value of chi-squared must be EQUAL TO or GREATER THAN the value that appears in the table.

4 Discuss the frustration–aggression hypothesis as a social psychological explanation of human aggression.

[16 marks]   AO1 = 6   AO3 = 10

The suggested paragraph starters below will help form your answer:

- The frustration–aggression hypothesis says that aggression is the result of… (AO1)
- This leads to the arousal of an aggressive drive, which… (AO1)
- After we have been aggressive, we experience catharsis. This is… (AO1)
- Sometimes it isn't possible to behave aggressively towards the source of our frustration, so instead we… (AO1)
- One strength of the frustration–aggression hypothesis is that it can be used to explain mass killings. For example… (AO3)
- A second strength of the frustration–aggression hypothesis is it can also explain violent behaviour in football fans… (AO3)
- However, a major weakness of the frustration–aggression hypothesis is that not all aggression is the result of frustration. For example… (AO3)
- Another weakness of the frustration–aggression hypothesis is that there is very little research support for the idea of catharsis. For example… (AO3)
- A final weakness of the frustration-aggression hypothesis is that it has been challenged by social learning theory. For example… (AO3)

⭐ Exam tip

Remember to elaborate each of your AO3 points by using, for example, the PEEL approach.

_____

_____

_____

_____

_____

_____

_____

_____

_____

_____

_____

_____

_____

_____

_____

_____

_____

_____

_____

_____

_____

_____

Social learning theory

Specification notes

Social psychological explanations of human aggression, including social learning theory as applied to human aggression.

Year 2 Student Book
Pages 238–239

---

1 Below are four statements about social learning theory. Which **one** statement is **false**?

Tick **one** box only.

[1 mark] AO1 = 1

A	Children learn about the consequences of aggressive behaviour by watching others being reinforced or punished.	
B	In order for social learning to take place, children must form mental representations in their social environment.	
C	Children primarily learn their aggressive responses through observation.	
D	Only direct experience is responsible for the acquisition of new behaviours.	

 Topic link

Social Learning Theory can be found on pages 128–129 of the Year 1 Student Book.

---

2 Outline social learning theory as a social psychological explanation for aggression.

[4 marks] AO1 = 4

Social learning theory says that we learn aggressive behaviour by _____

_____

If we watch someone else be rewarded for a behaviour, then we _____

_____

Social learning theory also uses the concept of a type of schema called a script. This is _____

_____

If our role model is someone we admire, then _____

_____

Exam tip

Remember to link your explanation of social learning theory to aggression.

---

3 Steve and Jim were discussing a research study on aggression. 'The study's practical message is clear,' said Steve. 'Children learn their behaviour from adults. If we are to have a more peaceful world, it starts with the way adults act around children.'

[4 marks] AO2 = 4

Using your knowledge of social learning theory, explain how the study could have given a 'clear practical message'.

Social learning theory says that we learn by _____

_____

If our role models are people we admire then _____

_____

_____

The study gives a clear practical message because _____

_____

_____

4 In a study conducted by Bandura *et al.* (1963) children saw an adult behave aggressively towards an inflated Bobo doll. The researchers found that, compared with a matched control group of children who had no prior exposure to the adult model, they were significantly more likely to behave aggressively towards the Bobo doll.

4(a)	[2 marks]	AO1 = 2
4(b)	[2 marks]	AO2 = 2
4(c)	[2 marks]	AO2 = 2
4(d)	[3 marks]	AO2 = 3

(a) Bandura *et al.* (1963) operationalised aggression in several ways. Explain why it is important to operationalise variables in psychological research.

_____

_____

_____

_____

(b) The children in the experimental conditions were matched with participants in the control condition. Explain how the participants might have been matched in this investigation.

_____

_____

_____

_____

⭐ **Exam tip**

Think about what might act as a confounding variable in this type of study.

(c) The researchers had independent observers record the aggression shown by the children. Explain why the researchers did not record the children's aggression themselves.

_____

_____

_____

_____

(d) Explain **one** way in which the researchers could have assessed the reliability of their observers' measurements.

_____

_____

_____

_____

_____

_____

⭐ **Exam tip**

Remember that reliability refers to the consistency of measurements.

5 Give **two** strengths of the social learning theory of human aggression.

[6 marks]	AO3 = 6

One strength of social learning theory is _____

_____

For example _____

_____

_____

A second strength of social learning theory is _____

_____

For example _____

_____

_____

---

6 Evaluate social learning theory as a social psychological explanation for aggression.

[6 marks]	AO3 = 6
[10 marks]	AO3 = 10

The suggested paragraph starters below will help form your answer:

- One strength of social learning theory as an explanation for aggression is that it can explain inconsistencies in people's use of aggression. For example… (AO3)
- Another strength of social learning theory is that it can explain cultural differences in aggression… (AO3)
- A third strength of social learning theory as an explanation for aggression is there are real-world applications. For example… (AO3)
- A final strength of social learning theory is that there is real-world support for its predictions. For example… (AO3)
- However, one major limitation of social learning theory is that there are methodological issues in the research supporting it. For example… (AO3)

Exam tip

This question requires you to evaluate social learning theory as an explanation for aggression, and does not require any outline or description of it. You must resist the temptation to offer AO1 on a question like this.

_____

_____

_____

_____

_____

_____

_____

_____

_____

_____

_____

_____

_____

_____

_____

_____

_____

_____

_____

_____

_____

Specification notes

Social psychological explanations of human aggression, including de-individuation.

Year 2 Student Book
Pages 240–241

---

1. Which **one** of the following statements best describes de-individuation?

   Tick **one** box only.

A	It is a psychological state in which people become autonomous.	
B	It is a psychological state in which people have lowered levels of self-evaluation.	
C	It is a state in which people have increased concerns about evaluation by others.	
D	It is a state in which self-control increases and people act in a more restrained manner.	

[1 mark] AO1 = 1

⭐ Exam tip

Multiple choice questions are a lot easier to answer if you first cross out any statement that you feel confident does not describe de-individuation. That narrows down your options when picking the one correct answer.

---

2. Describe how de-individuation explains human aggression.

De-individuation is when people _____

_____

This can happen when we are _____

_____

Usually, we don't act aggressively because _____

_____

De-individuation means that we feel _____

_____

[4 marks] AO1 = 4

⭐ Exam tip

Remember that 'describe' questions are AO1 only.

---

3. Outline **one** limitation of de-individuation as an explanation of human aggression.

One limitation of de-individuation as an explanation of human aggression is that disinhibition and antisocial behaviour are not more common in large groups.

For example, Postmes and Spears _____

_____

_____

De-individuation could lead to either_____

_____

_____

This suggests that_____

_____

[4 marks] AO3 = 4

⭐ Exam tip

This question asks you to outline a limitation of de-individuation, so writing about a strength won't get you any marks.

4. A researcher proposed that people feel more anonymous in a big city than in a small town, because people are more likely to know one another in a small town. Consequently, de-individuation is more likely to occur in a big city than in a small town. To test this, he parked a car in the street of a big city, and parked an identical car in the street of a small town. Both cars had their number plates removed and their bonnets raised in order to make it appear they had been abandoned. Research assistants filmed people's behaviour from hidden locations. Within a day, the car in the big city had most of its parts removed. However, even after a week nothing had been taken from the car in the small town. Indeed, on the day it rained, a passer-by lowered the car's bonnet to protect its engine!

4(a)	[3 marks]	AO2 = 3
4(b)	[2 marks]	AO1 = 2
4(c)	[3 marks]	AO2 = 3

 Topic link

You can find out more about observational techniques on pages 198–199 of the Year 1 Student Book.

(a) Using information in the item above, explain the difference between overt and covert observation.

_____

_____

_____

_____

_____

_____

(b) Explain **one** weakness of **either** overt **or** covert observation.

_____

_____

_____

(c) Write a suitable hypothesis for the study outlined in the item above.

_____

_____

_____

_____

_____

_____

5 Discuss the de-individuation explanation of human aggression.

[16 marks] AO1 = 6 AO3 = 10

The suggested paragraph starters below will help form your answer:

- De-individuation is when people… (AO1)
- This can happen when we are… (AO1)
- Usually, we don't act aggressively because… (AO1)
- De-individuation means that we feel… (AO1)
- One strength of the de-individuation explanation comes from research conducted by Rehm *et al*. They… (AO3)
- A second strength of the de-individuation explanation comes from studies of baiting crowds. For example… (AO3)
- A third strength of de-individuation is that there is anthropological support for it. For example… (AO3)
- However, one limitation of the de-individuation explanation is that there are gender differences in how people respond under de-individuated conditions… (AO3)
- A second limitation of the de-individuation explanation is that disinhibition and antisocial behaviour are not more common in large groups… (AO3)

_____

_____

_____

_____

_____

_____

_____

_____

_____

_____

_____

_____

_____

_____

_____

_____

_____

Specification notes
Institutional aggression in the context of prisons: dispositional and situational explanations.

Year 2 Student Book
Pages 242–243

---

1 Which **one** of the following statements about dispositional and situational explanations of aggression in prisons is **false**?

Tick **one** box only.

[1 mark]   AO1 = 1

A	The deprivation model is a situational explanation which focuses on the stressful nature of the prison itself.	
B	Situational explanations claim that aggression in prisons is caused by the prison context.	
C	Dispositional explanations claim that aggression in prisons is caused by the characteristics of people in prisons.	
D	Dispositional explanations emphasise the role of overcrowding, temperature, and noise in causing aggression in prisons.	

---

2 Evaluate situational explanations of institutional aggression.

[4 marks]   AO3 = 4

One strength of situational explanations of institutional aggression is that they have real-world applications. For example, Wilson _____

_____

_____

One limitation is that the link between situational factors and aggression has not always been supported by research. For example, Harer and Steffensmeier _____

_____

_____

> ★ **Exam tip**
>
> As there are only 4 marks available, you can choose to make one evaluation point in more detail, or two evaluation points in less detail.

---

3 Outline the dispositional explanation of institutional aggression and give **one** limitation of this explanation.

[6 marks]   AO1 = 4   AO3 = 2

The importation model says that institutional aggression occurs because _____

_____

_____

For example, an important determinant of prison misconduct is _____

_____

_____

_____

However, one limitation of the dispositional explanation is that the importation model's claims about pre-prison gang membership has been questioned _____

_____

_____

_____

4 Several variables have been linked with aggression in prisons. In one study, researchers looked at the association between murder rates and time of year. Using data obtained from prison authorities, they recorded the number of murders that occurred in 'summer', 'autumn', 'winter', and 'spring' in 20 American prisons. Their findings are shown in the table below.

4(a)	[2 marks]	AO2 = 2
4(b)	[2 marks]	AO2 = 2
4(c)	[3 marks]	AO2 = 3
4(d)	[3 marks]	AO2 = 3

	'Summer'	'Autumn'	'Winter'	'Spring'
Number of murders committed	35	10	8	22

(a) The data collected in this study is secondary data. Explain what is meant by secondary data.

_____

_____

_____

_____

(b) Identify the independent and dependent variables in this study.

_____

_____

_____

_____

(c) Write a non-directional hypothesis for this study.

_____

_____

_____

_____

_____

_____

(d) The researchers used a chi-squared test to analyse their findings. Give **three** reasons why this was an appropriate test to use.

_____

_____

_____

_____

_____

_____

Exam tip

Remember that the dependent variable is the variable that the researcher measures, and the independent variable is the variable that the researcher manipulates.

Exam tip

Think about whether the researchers are looking for a difference or a correlation, the type of design they have used, and the level of measurement of their data.

5 A prison warden was concerned about prisoners using mobile phones. She asked an electronics expert to block all mobile phone signals inside the prison. The system was successful, and calls could neither be made nor received by the prisoners. Within a month, assaults on prison officers increased dramatically.

Use your knowledge of explanations of institutional aggression to explain why the number of assaults on prison officers might have increased dramatically.

The deprivation model says that _____

_____

For example, deprivation of goods and services leads to _____

_____

This then results in _____

_____

As the prisoners could no longer use their mobile phones, they _____

_____

Exam tip

Remember to link your answer back to the scenario to gain all the marks.

---

6 Outline and evaluate explanations of institutional aggression.

The suggested paragraph starters below will help form your answer:

- The deprivation model says that institutional aggression occurs because… (AO1)
- The importation model says that institutional aggression occurs because… (AO1)
- There is research support for the deprivation model. For example, McCorkle *et al.* … (AO1)
- One practical advantage of the deprivation model is that it can be used to reduce aggression in prisons. For example… (AO3)
- However, the link between situational factors and aggression has not always been supported by research. For example… (AO3)
- The importation model has also been supported by research findings. For example… (AO3)
- However, the importation model's claims about pre-prison gang membership has been questioned. For example… (AO3)

Exam tip

This question asks you to write about explanations, rather than just one explanation. If you only write about one, you are 'partially performing' and cannot receive full marks.

_____

_____

_____

_____

_____

_____

_____

_____

_____

_____

_____

_____

Specification notes

Media influences on aggression, including the effects of computer games.

Year 2 Student Book
Pages 244–245

---

1 Which **one** of the following methods of investigating media influences on aggression involves an independent variable being manipulated by a researcher?

[1 mark]   AO1 = 1

Tick **one** box only.

A	Studies looking at the relationship between how much television children watch and how aggressive they are.	
B	Studies tracking children over time in order to assess the impact of early experiences on their behaviour later in life.	
C	Studies looking at the effects of watching either non-violent or violent television on aggressive behaviour.	
D	Studies aggregating the findings from many investigations into the influence of the media on aggressive behaviour.	

---

2 Outline **one** study that has investigated the effects of computer games on aggression.

[4 marks]   AO1 = 4

Greitemeyer and Mügge carried out _____

_____

_____

_____

They found that _____

_____

_____

_____

⭐ **Exam tip**

For full marks, you need to explain what the researchers did and what they found.

---

3 Outline **one** criticism of research into the effects of computer games on aggression.

[4 marks]   AO3 = 4

One criticism is that game difficulty may be more important in causing aggression than _____

_____

For example, Przybylski *et al.* suggest _____

_____

They found that _____

_____

This means that _____

_____

⭐ **Exam tip**

Even though the question says 'outline', it's asking you to 'outline one criticism', which means this is an AO3 rather than an AO1 question.

4. Researchers installed automated time-lapse recording equipment in the televisions of ten families. Recording began when the television was switched on and stopped when it was switched off. One of the cameras used a wide-angled lens to record people's behaviour in the room where the television was. Some of the study's findings are shown in the table below:

4(a)	[2 marks]	AO2 = 2
4(b)	[2 marks]	AO2 = 2
4(c)	[2 marks]	AO2 = 2
4(d)	[1 mark]	AO2 = 1
4(e)	[2 marks]	AO2 = 2

Family	% of time the TV was actually being watched by the family when it was switched on	Number of hours children spend watching TV per week
1	63	6
2	75	7
3	59	7
4	54	9
5	60	5
6	17	6
7	50	7
8	47	8
9	67	9
10	65	10

(a) Calculate the mean percentage of time that families actually spend watching the TV per week. Show your calculations.

_____

_____

_____

_____

> **Exam tip**
>
> Questions relating to mathematical skills may need you to know how to calculate percentages and fractions.

(b) Using the data in the table above, outline **one** weakness of the mean as a measure of central tendency.

_____

_____

_____

_____

(c) Calculate the modal number of hours children spend watching TV per week. Show your calculations.

_____

_____

_____

_____

(d) Name **one** measure of dispersion that could be used in this study.

_____

_____

(e) Outline **one** ethical issue that should have been taken into consideration in this study.

_____

_____

_____

_____

Exam tip

Make sure the issue that you outline is relevant to the study that has been described.

[16 marks] AO1 = 6 AO3 = 10

5 Discuss research into media influences on aggression.

The suggested paragraph starters below will help form your answer:

- Experiments show that people who watch violent scenes have more aggressive thoughts and behaviour. For example, Bjorkqvist… (AO1)
- Bushman and Heusemann's meta-analysis found… (AO1)
- Experiments show short-term increases in physiological arousal and hostility following violent video game play. For example, Anderson and Dill… (AO1)
- One methodological issue in studying media influences on aggression concerns the samples used. For example… (AO3)
- A second methodological issue concerns the measurement of aggression. For example… (AO3)
- Research also suggests that there are several causal variables that might be involved in computer game aggression. For example, Ferguson *et al.* … (AO3)
- Other research suggests that game difficulty is a more important variable in causing aggressive behaviour. For example… (AO3)
- A final issue is that the relationship between media violence and aggressive behaviour has been overstated. For example… (AO3)

Exam tip

Remember to check how many AO1 and AO3 marks are available before you start writing.

_____

_____

_____

_____

_____

_____

_____

_____

_____

_____

_____

_____

_____

_____

_____

_____

_____

Specification notes

The role of desensitisation, disinhibition, and cognitive priming.

Year 2 Student Book
Pages 246–247

[1 mark] AO1 = 1

1 Which **one** of the following best describes cognitive priming as an explanation of media influences on aggression?

Tick **one** box only.

A	Observing media violence can lead to its imitation, especially if the violent behaviour is seen to be rewarded.	
B	Media violence activates thoughts or ideas about violence which activate other aggressive thoughts through their association in memory pathways.	
C	Media violence leads to aggressive behaviour by removing anxiety about behaving violently.	
D	Exposure to violent behaviour legitimises violence by undermining the social sanctions that usually inhibit such behaviour.	

[4 marks] AO1 = 4

2 Outline the disinhibition explanation of media influences on aggression.

This explanation says that watching or playing violent media may change our usual standards

_____

Exposure to violent media can _____

_____

This can have immediate effects, such as _____

_____

It can also have long-term effects, such as _____

_____

⭐ **Exam tip**

Three explanations are named on the specification, so a question could be asked directly about any of them.

[6 marks] AO1 = 3 AO3 = 3

3 Outline the desensitisation explanation of media influences of aggression and give **one** strength of this explanation.

SAMPLE ANSWER: *The desensitisation explanation says that under normal conditions, anxiety about aggression inhibits its use. Media violence, however, may lead to aggression by removing this anxiety. The more violence that is watched, the more acceptable aggression is seen to be.*
There is research support for the desensitisation explanation of media influences on aggression. For example, Carnegey et al. found that playing violent video games produces physiological desensitisation. Participants who had played a violent computer game had a lower heart rate and skin conductance response while viewing a video clip of real-life violence, compared to the control group. This shows that desensitisation can occur after watching violent media.

4. In a study of the desensitisation explanation of media influences, researchers randomly allocated participants who claimed not to play computer games to one of two groups. One group played a violent computer game, and the other group a non-violent computer game for the same amount of time. Both groups then watched a ten-minute film containing extremely violent scenes. The researchers compared changes in physiological arousal of the two groups and found a significant difference between them.

4(a)	[2 marks]	AO2 = 2
4(b)	[3 marks]	AO2 = 3
4(c)	[3 marks]	AO2 = 3
4(d)	[2 marks]	AO3 = 2

(a) Identify the independent and dependent variables in this study.

_____

_____

_____

_____

(b) Suggest a directional hypothesis for this study.

_____

_____

_____

_____

_____

_____

Exam tip

Remember that directional hypotheses state the direction of the predicted effect.

(c) Explain how the researchers could have randomly allocated participants to the two groups.

_____

_____

_____

_____

_____

_____

Exam tip

This is not a general question about how to carry out random sampling, but a specific one about how random allocation could have been carried out within this study.

(d) The study was conducted in a laboratory setting. Outline **one** advantage of conducting research in this way.

_____

_____

_____

_____

Topic link

You can find out more about different types of experiment on pages 186–189 of the Year 1 Student Book.

⑤ Discuss **one or more** explanations of media influences on aggression.

[16 marks] | AO1 = 6 | AO3 = 10

The suggested paragraph starters below will help form your answer:

- The desensitisation explanation says that… (AO1)
- The disinhibition explanation says that… (AO1)
- Media influences on aggression can also be explained by cognitive priming. This is… (AO1)
- One strength for the desensitisation explanation is that it is supported by research. For example, Carnegey *et al.* … (AO3)
- However, one limitation of this explanation is that desensitisation is sometimes adaptive. For example… (AO3)
- One limitation of the disinhibition effect is that it depends on other factors, such as the individual, or the context. For example… (AO3)
- A second limitation of disinhibition is that it is less likely in situations where violent behaviour has negative consequences. For example… (AO3)
- A strength of cognitive priming is that it has research support. For example… (AO3)

 Exam tip

You need to make sure that each of your evaluation points links back to the question.

 Exam tip

This question asks you to write about one or more explanations. This means that you can take a 'depth' approach and write about one explanation in detail, or you can take a 'breadth' approach and write about more than one explanation in less detail.

Notes